Non-verbal Reasoning

Assessment Papers

5–6 years

OXFORD
UNIVERSITY PRESS

UNIVERSITY PRESS

Great Clarendon Street, Oxford, OX2 6DP, United Kingdom

Oxford University Press is a department of the University of Oxford.
It furthers the University's objective of excellence in research,
scholarship, and education by publishing worldwide. Oxford is
a registered trade mark of Oxford University Press in the UK and in
certain other countries

British Library Cataloguing in Publication Data
Data available

978-0-19-274220-9

10 9 8

Paper used in the production of this book is a natural, recyclable
product made from wood grown in sustainable forests.
The manufacturing process conforms to the environmental
regulations of the country of origin.

Printed in Great Britain by Ashford Colour Press Ltd, Gosport, Hants

Acknowledgements

The publishers would like to thank the following for permissions to
use copyright material:

Page make-up: eMC Design Ltd
Illustrations: Nigel Kitching; OKS Prepress, India
Cover illustrations: Lo Cole

Although we have made every effort to trace and contact all
copyright holders before publication this has not been possible in all
cases. If notified, the publisher will rectify any errors or omissions at
the earliest opportunity.

Links to third party websites are provided by Oxford in good faith
and for information only. Oxford disclaims any responsibility for
the materials contained in any third party website referenced in
this work.

Introduction

What is Bond?

This book is part of the Bond range of assessment papers for non-verbal reasoning, which provides thorough and continuous practice of all the key non-verbal reasoning content from ages 5 to 12. Bond's non-verbal reasoning resources are ideal preparation for many different kinds of tests and exams – from SATs to the 11$^+$ and other secondary school selection exams.

What does this book cover?

Non-verbal reasoning questions can be grouped into five distinct categories: identifying shapes, missing shapes, rotating shapes, coded shapes and logic. This book lays the earliest foundations through practising six basic question types: finding the odd one out, finding which one belongs, identifying identical patterns, completing a visual sequence, completing a pattern, and completing a visual analogy. The questions at this level involve pictures and shapes so that they are similar to the picture puzzles with which children may already be familiar.

The age given on the cover is for guidance only. As the papers are designed to be reasonably challenging for the year group, any one child may find him or herself working above or below the stated age. The important thing is that children are always encouraged by their performance. Working at the right level is the key to this.

What does the book contain?

- Eight papers – each paper contains 15 questions.
- Scoring devices – there are scoring boxes in the margins and a progress chart at the back of the book. Encouraging the child to colour in the chart as they go along and to try to beat their score can be very motivating.
- Answers – these are located in an easily removed central pull-out section.

How can you use this book?

One of the great strengths of the Bond range of assessment papers is their flexibility. They can be used at home, school and by tutors to:

- provide regular verbal reasoning practice in bite-sized chunks
- highlight strengths and weaknesses in the core skills
- identify individual needs
- set homework
- set timed practice tests – allow about 15 minutes.

Remember, more support, advice, information and free resources are available at www.bond11plus.co.uk.

Paper 1

Which is the odd one out? Circle the letter.

Example

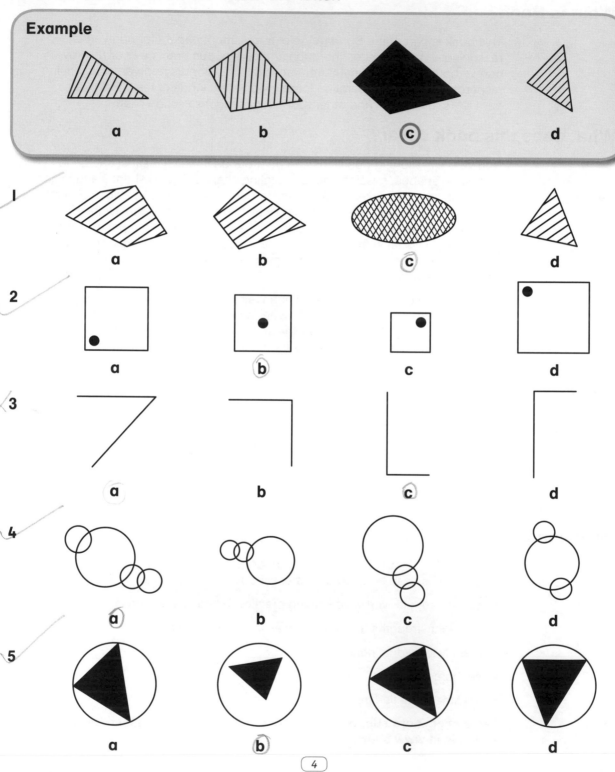

Which one comes next? Circle the letter.

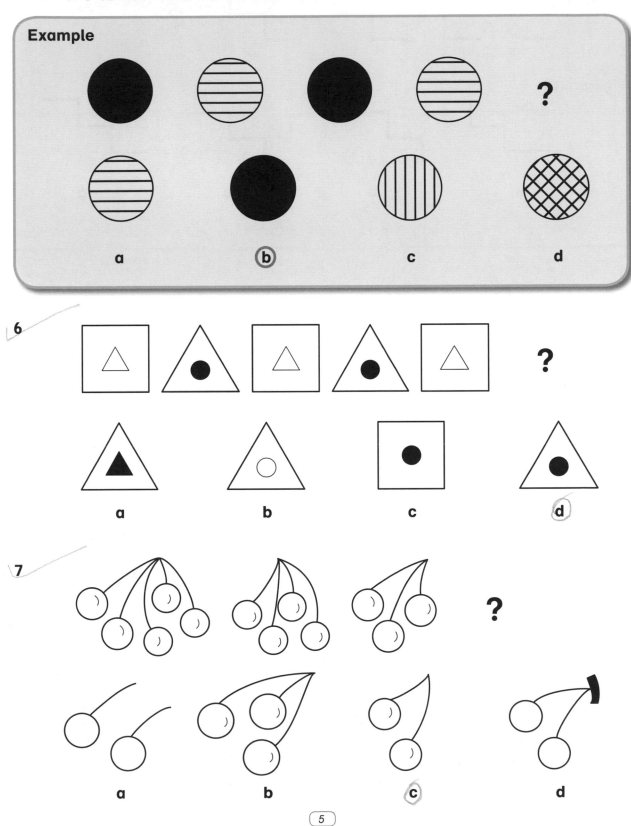

Example

a   **(b)**   c   d

6

a   b   c   **(d)**

7

a   b   **(c)**   d

8

a   b   c   d

9

a   b   c   d

10

a   b   c   d

Which one completes the pattern? Circle the letter.

Example

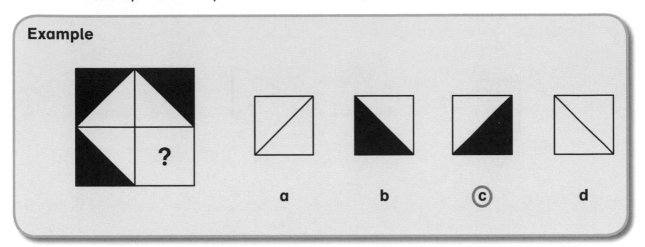

a   b   c   d

11

12

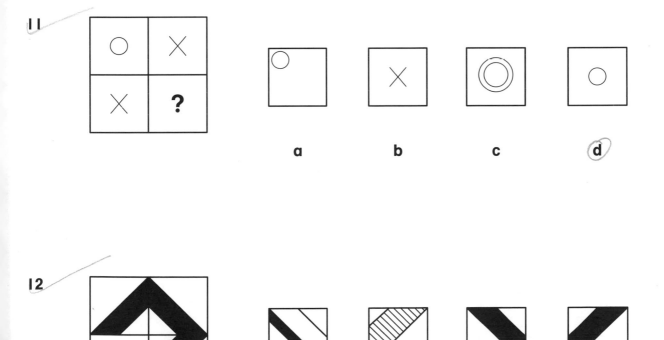

a   b   c   d

13

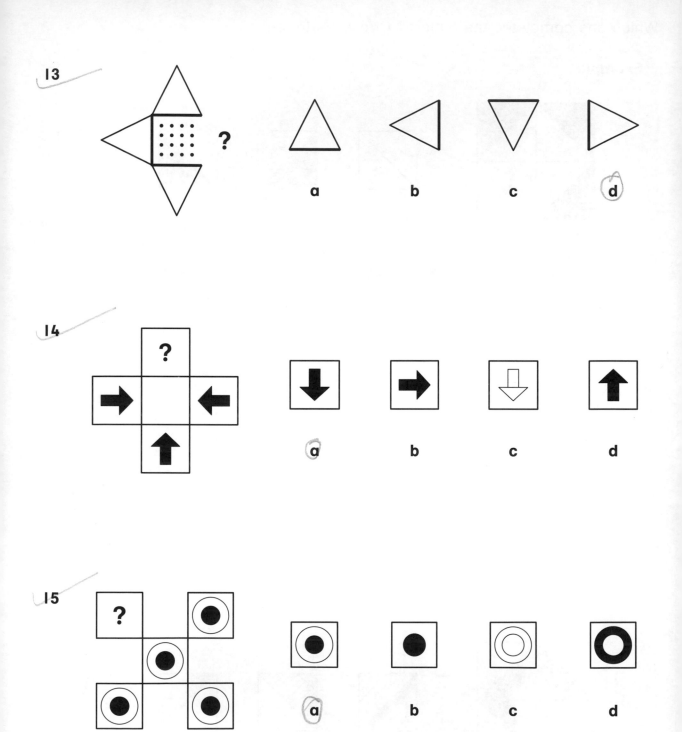

a b c **d**

14

?

a b c d

15

?

a b c d

Paper 2

Which is the odd one out? Circle the letter.

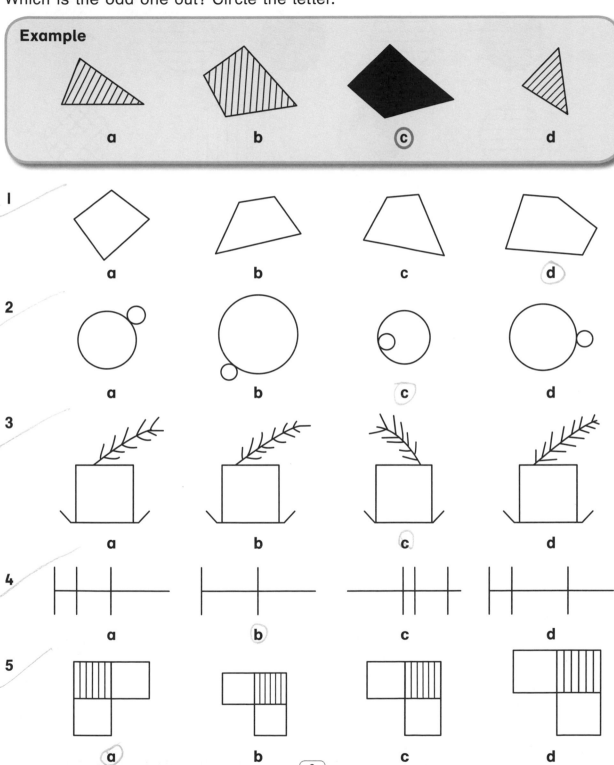

Example

a   b   ⓒ   d

1.   a   b   c   d

2.   a   b   c   d

3.   a   b   c   d

4.   a   b   c   d

5.   a   b   c   d

Which one comes next? Circle the letter.

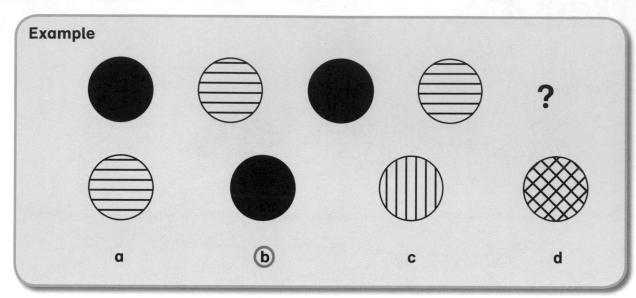

Example

a   **ⓑ**   c   d

6

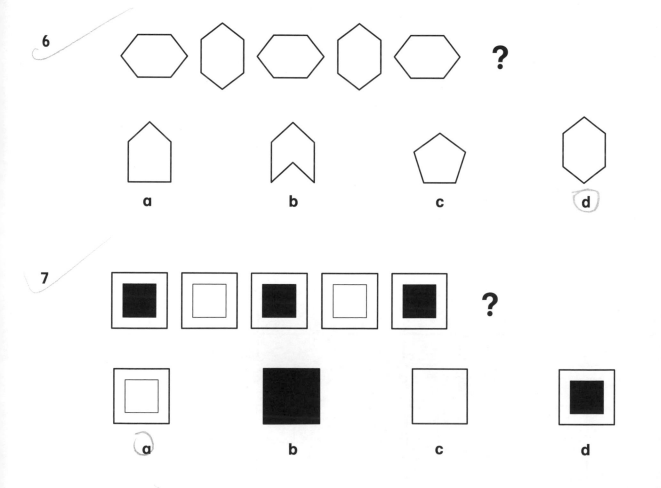

a   b   c   **ⓓ**

7

ⓐ   b   c   d

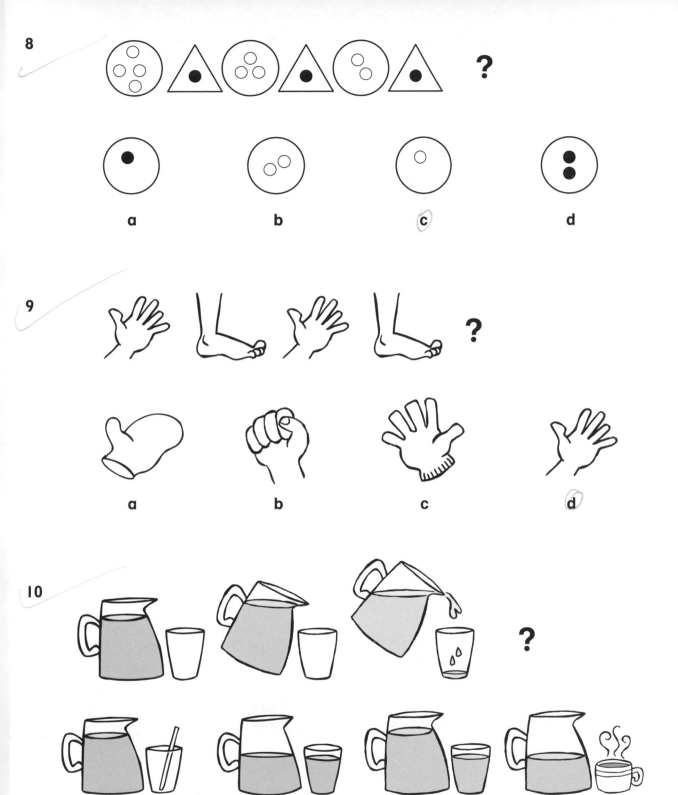

8

a   b   c   d

9

a   b   c   d

10

a   b   c   d

Which one is the same as the one on the left? Circle the letter.

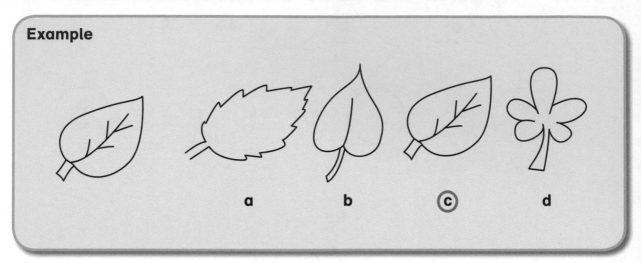

a   b   ⓒ   d

11

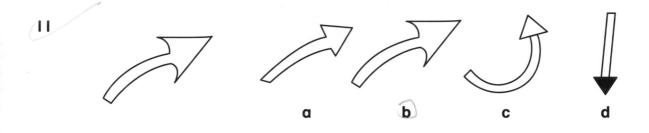

a   b   c   d

12

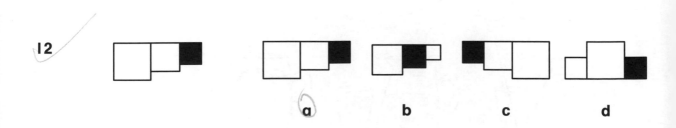

a   b   c   d

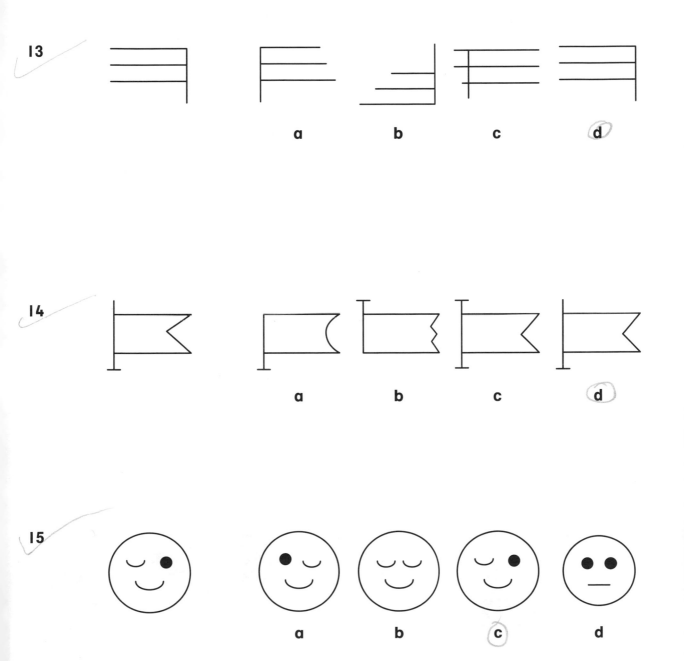

13

a   b   c   (d)

14

a   b   c   (d)

15

a   b   (c)   d

Paper 3

Which one belongs to the group? Circle the letter.

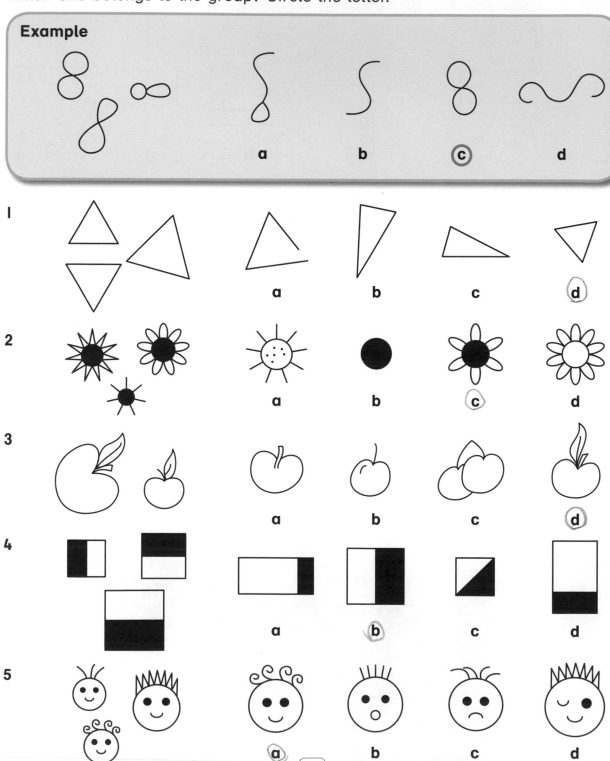

Example

a   b   ⓒ   d

1   a   b   c   ⓓ

2   a   b   ⓒ   d

3   a   b   c   ⓓ

4   a   ⓑ   c   d

5   ⓐ   b   c   d

14

Which one comes next? Circle the letter.

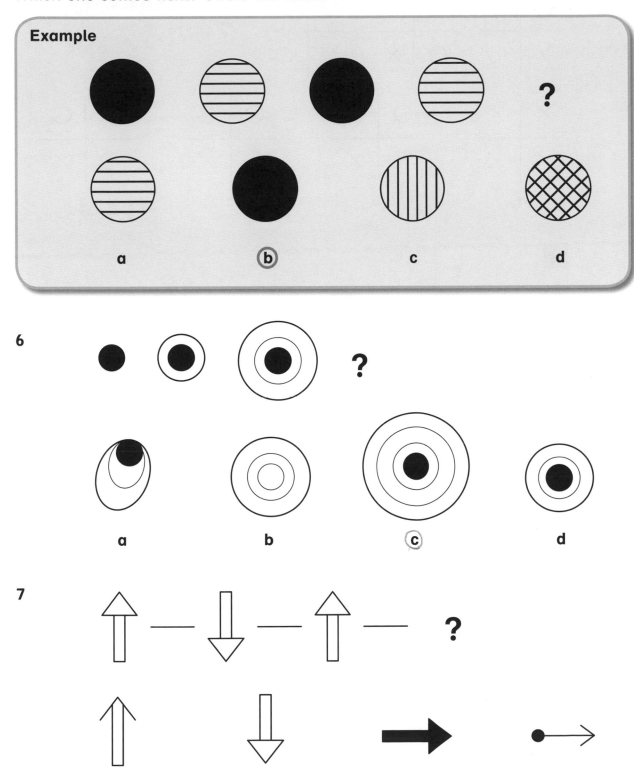

8

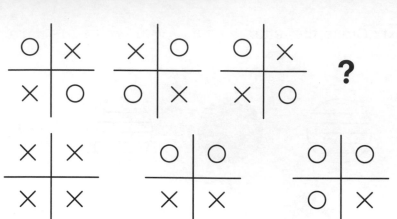

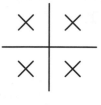
a

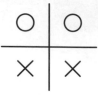
b

c

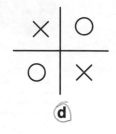
d

9

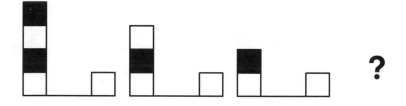

a

b

c

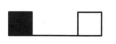
d

10

a

b

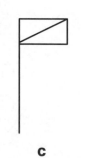
c

d

Which one completes the second pair in the same way as the first pair?
Circle the letter.

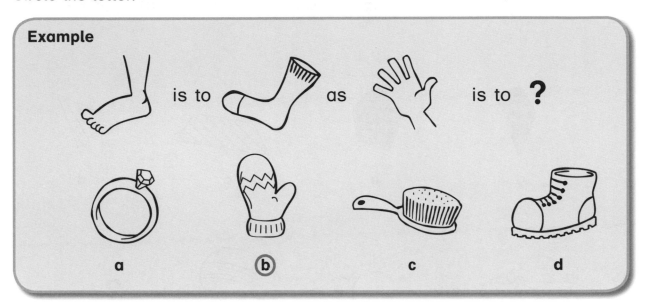

Example

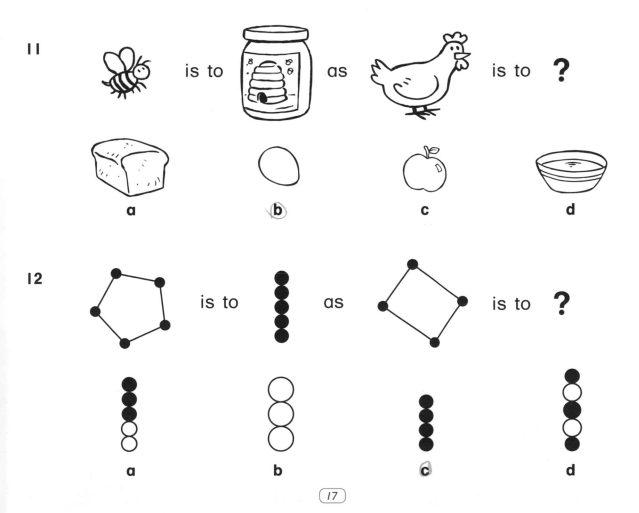

13

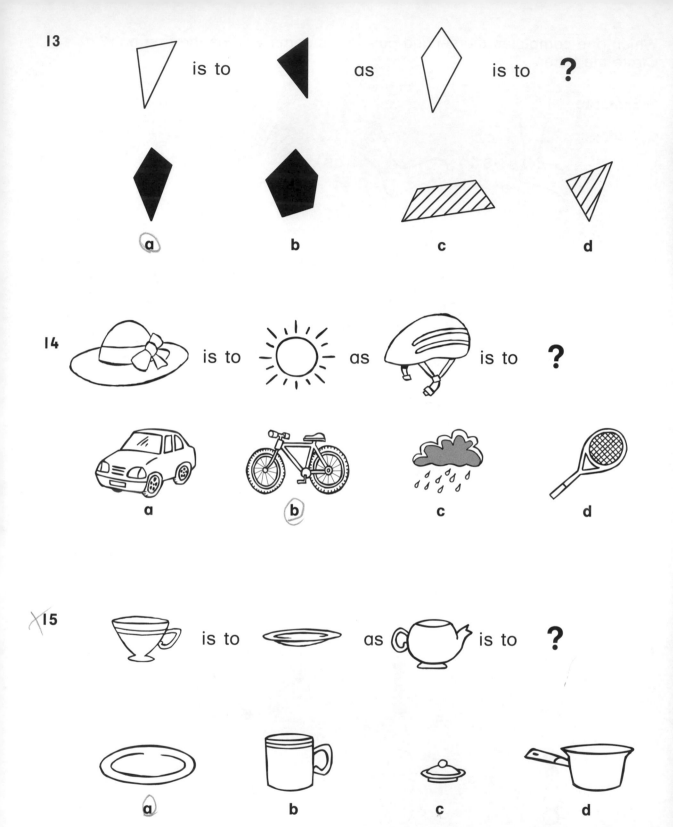

is to ... as ... is to **?**

a   b   c   d

14

is to ... as ... is to **?**

a   b   c   d

15

is to ... as ... is to **?**

a   b   c   d

Paper 4

Which one belongs to the group? Circle the letter.

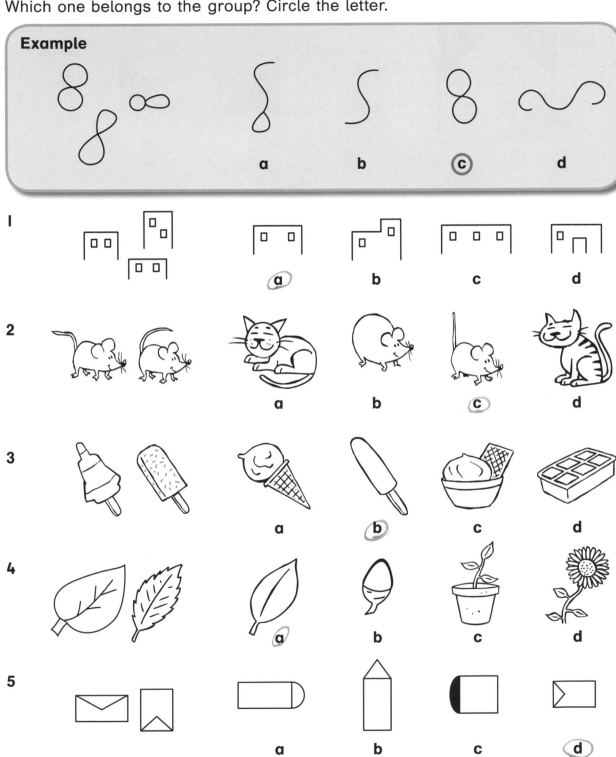

Example

a   b   c   d

1   a   b   c   d

2   a   b   c   d

3   a   b   c   d

4   a   b   c   d

5   a   b   c   d

Which one completes the pattern? Circle the letter.

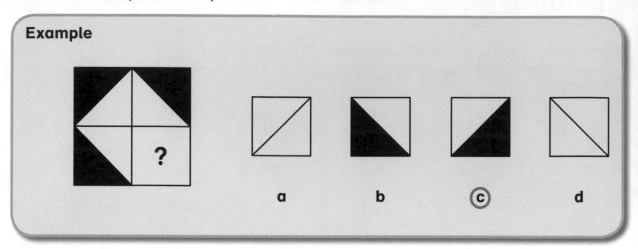

Example

a b © d

6

?

a b c d

7

?

a b © d

8

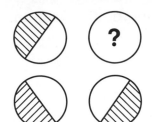
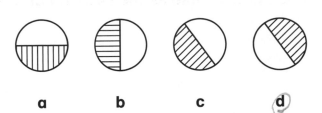

a   b   c   d

9

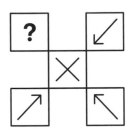
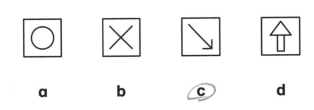

a   b   c   d

10

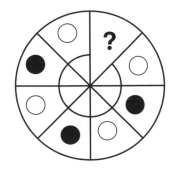
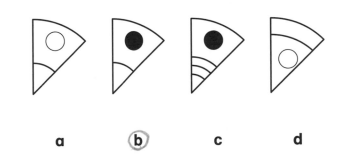

a   b   c   d

Which one completes the second pair in the same way as the first pair?
Circle the letter.

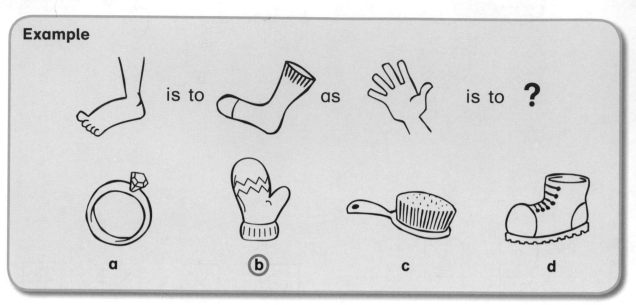

Example

foot is to sock as hand is to **?**

a ring   **b** mitten   c brush   d boot

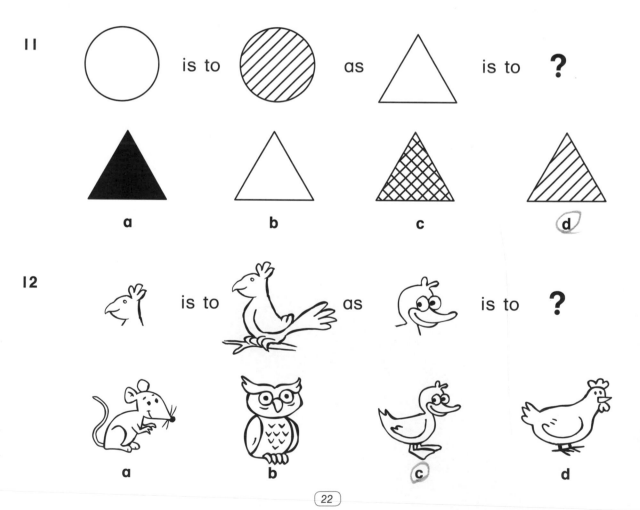

11

circle is to shaded circle as triangle is to **?**

a   b   c   d

12

mouse is to bird as duck is to **?**

a   b   c   d

Paper 1

1 c
2 b
3 a
4 a
5 b
6 d
7 c
8 d
9 c
10 d
11 d
12 c
13 d
14 a
15 a

Paper 2

1 d
2 c
3 c
4 b
5 a
6 d
7 a
8 c
9 d
10 b
11 b
12 a
13 d
14 d
15 c

Paper 3

1	d
2	c
3	d
4	b
5	a
6	c
7	b
8	d
9	c
10	d
11	b
12	c
13	a
14	b
15	c

Paper 4

1	a
2	c
3	b
4	a
5	d
6	b
7	c
8	d
9	c
10	b
11	d
12	c
13	b
14	d
15	a

Paper 5

1 c
2 b
3 c
4 d
5 d
6 c
7 d
8 b
9 b
10 a
11 b
12 c
13 a
14 a
15 c

Paper 6

1 a
2 d
3 d
4 a
5 c
6 b
7 c
8 d
9 c
10 a
11 d
12 b
13 b
14 c
15 b

Paper 7

1	b
2	c
3	b
4	c
5	d
6	a
7	d
8	d
9	b
10	a
11	d
12	c
13	d
14	a
15	c

Paper 8

1	c
2	c
3	a
4	d
5	b
6	b
7	c
8	d
9	b
10	a
11	d
12	c
13	b
14	c
15	d

13

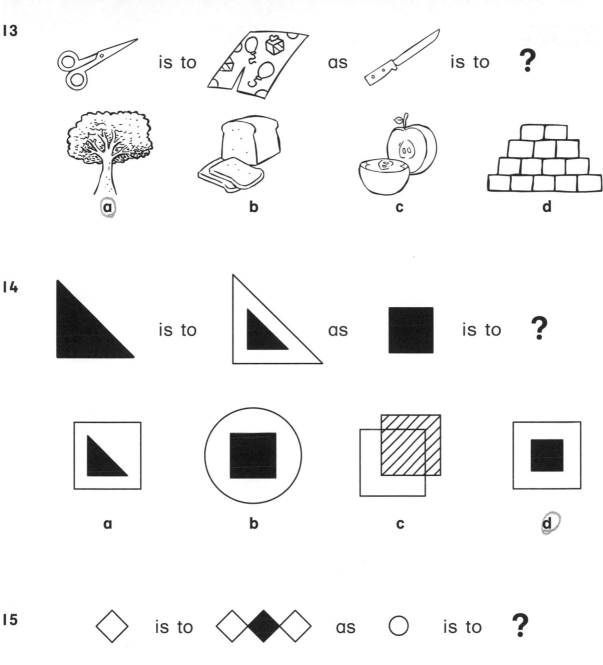

14

15

Paper 5

Which is the odd one out? Circle the letter.

Example

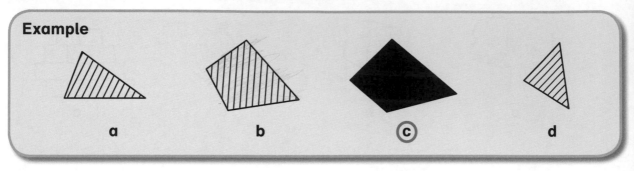

a   b   ⓒ   d

1

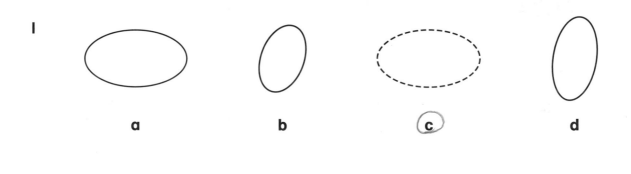

a   b   c   d

2

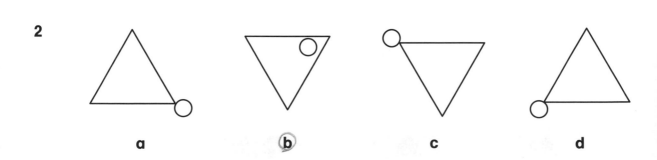

a   b   c   d

3

a   b   c   d

4

a   b   c   d

5

a   b   c   d

Which one is the same as the one on the left? Circle the letter.

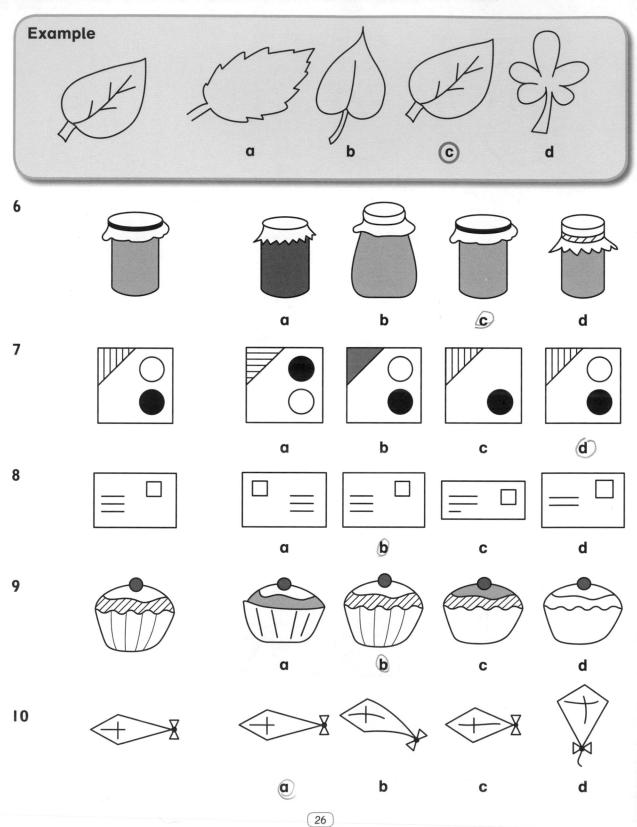

Example

a   b   ⓒ   d

6

a   b   ⓒ   d

7

a   b   c   ⓓ

8

a   ⓑ   c   d

9

a   ⓑ   c   d

10

ⓐ   b   c   d

Which one completes the second pair in the same way as the first pair?
Circle the letter.

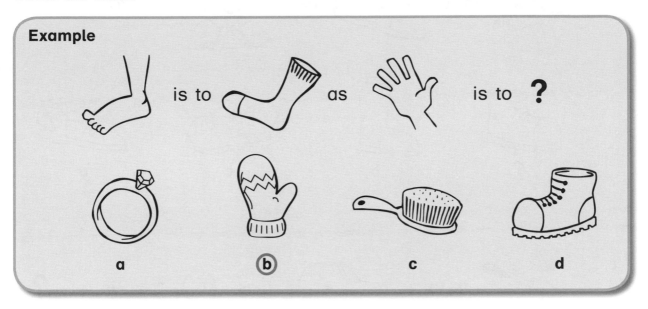

Example

is to ... as ... is to **?**

a   **ⓑ**   c   d

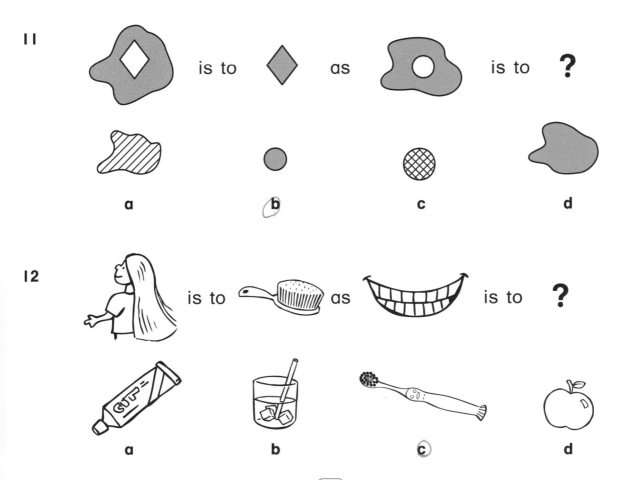

11

is to ... as ... is to **?**

a   b   c   d

12

is to ... as ... is to **?**

a   b   c   d

13

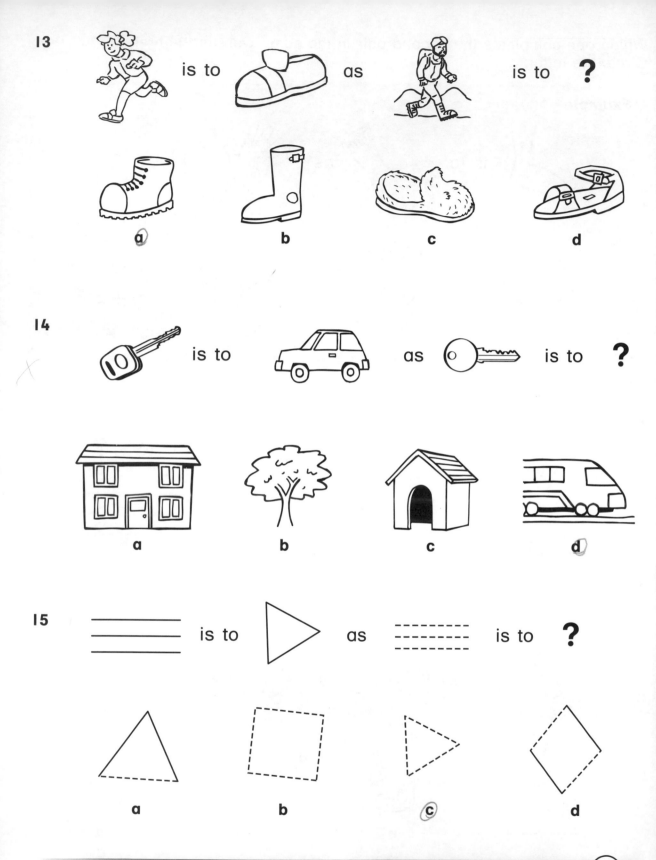

is to ... as ... is to **?**

a   b   c   d

14

is to ... as ... is to **?**

a   b   c   d

15

is to ... as ... is to **?**

a   b   c   d

Paper 6

Which is the odd one out? Circle the letter.

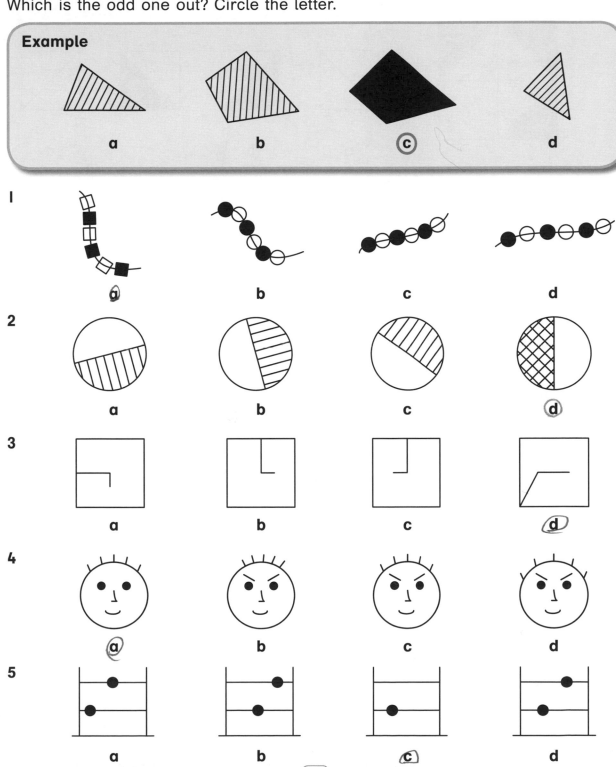

Example

a   b   c   d

1   a   b   c   d

2   a   b   c   d

3   a   b   c   d

4   a   b   c   d

5   a   b   c   d

29

Which one completes the pattern? Circle the letter.

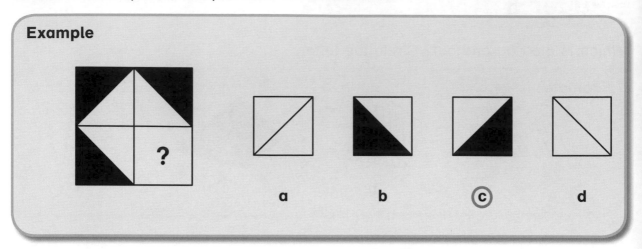

Example

a   b   c   d

6

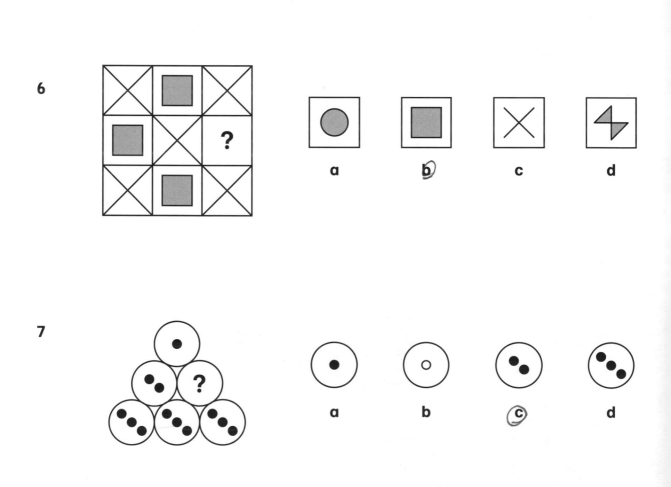

a   b   c   d

7

a   b   c   d

8

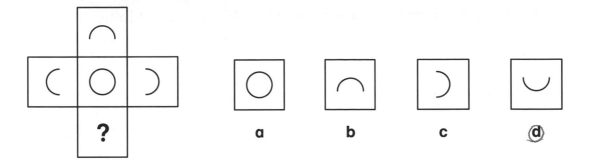

a b c d

9

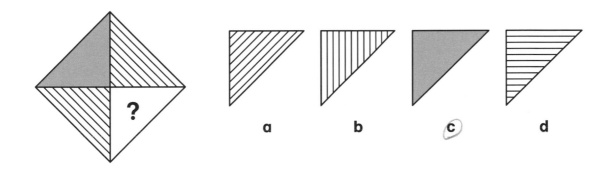

a b c d

10

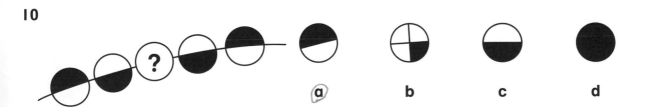

a b c d

31

Which one is the same as the one on the left? Circle the letter.

Example

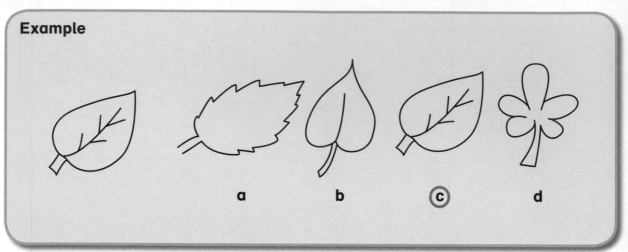

a b ⓒ d

11

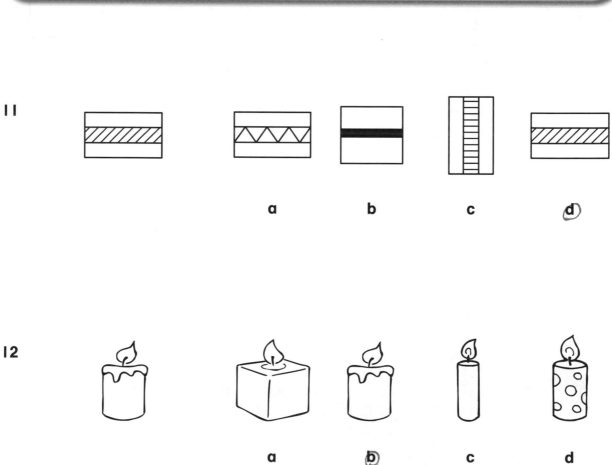

a b c d

12

a b c d

13

a b c d

14

a b c d

15

a b c d

Paper 7

Which one belongs to the group? Circle the letter.

Example

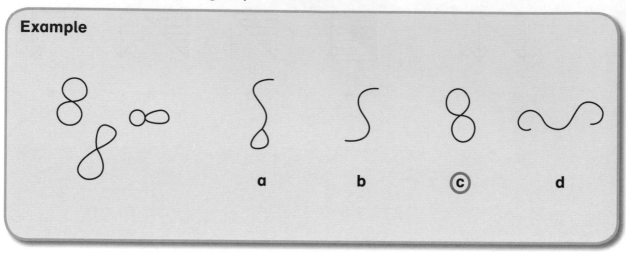

a   b   (c)   d

1

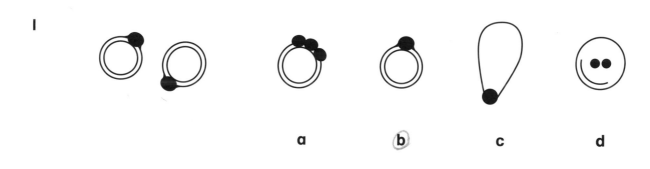

a   (b)   c   d

2

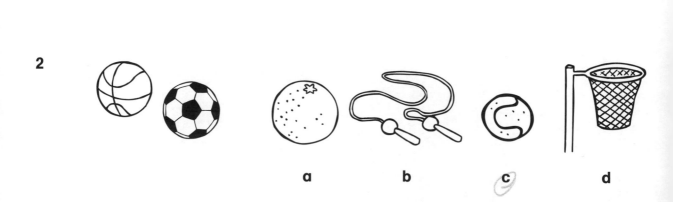

a   b   c   d

3

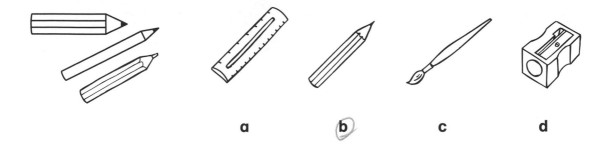

a b c d

4

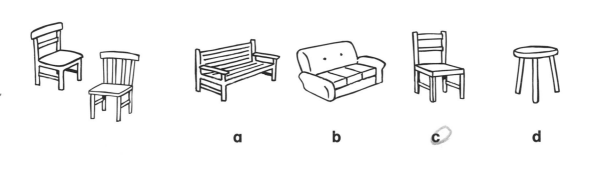

a b c d

5

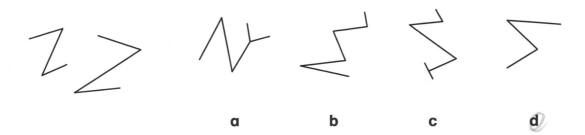

a b c d

Which one comes next? Circle the letter.

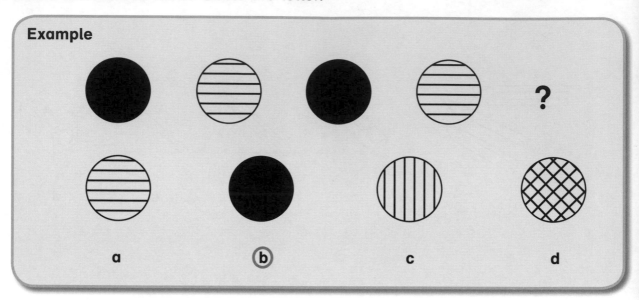

Example

a   (b)   c   d

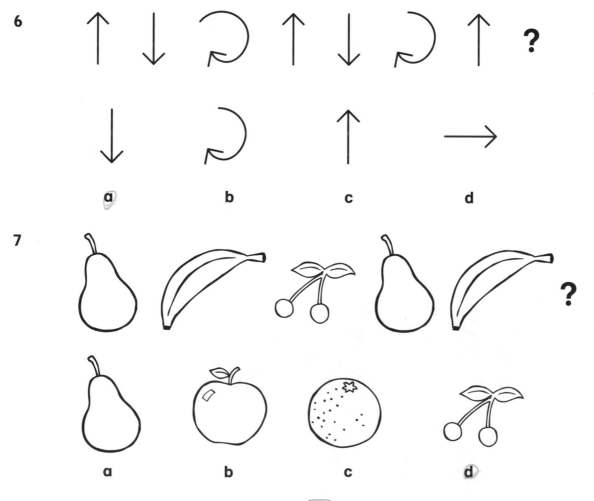

6

a   b   c   d

7

a   b   c   d

36

8

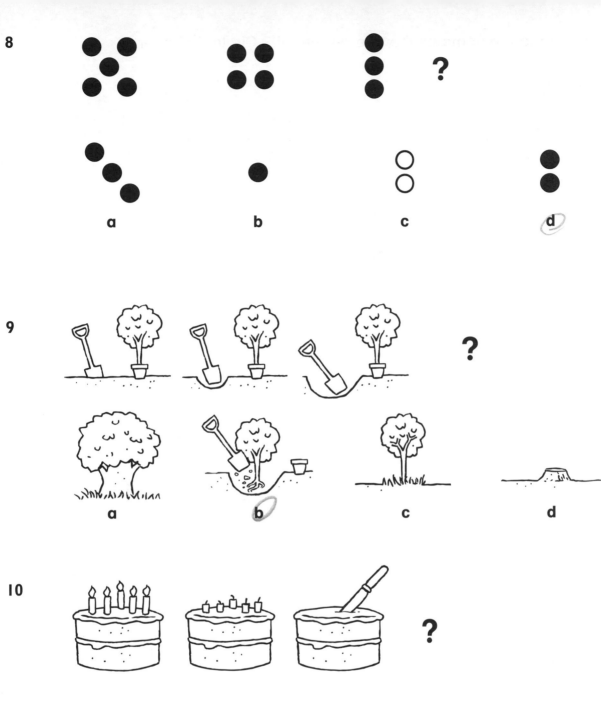

a b c **d**

9

a **b** c d

10

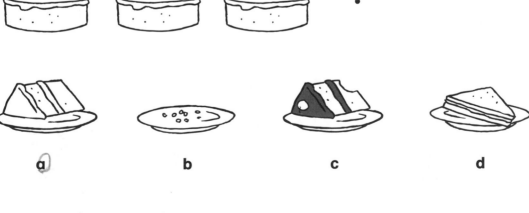

a b c d

Which one is the same as the one on the left? Circle the letter.

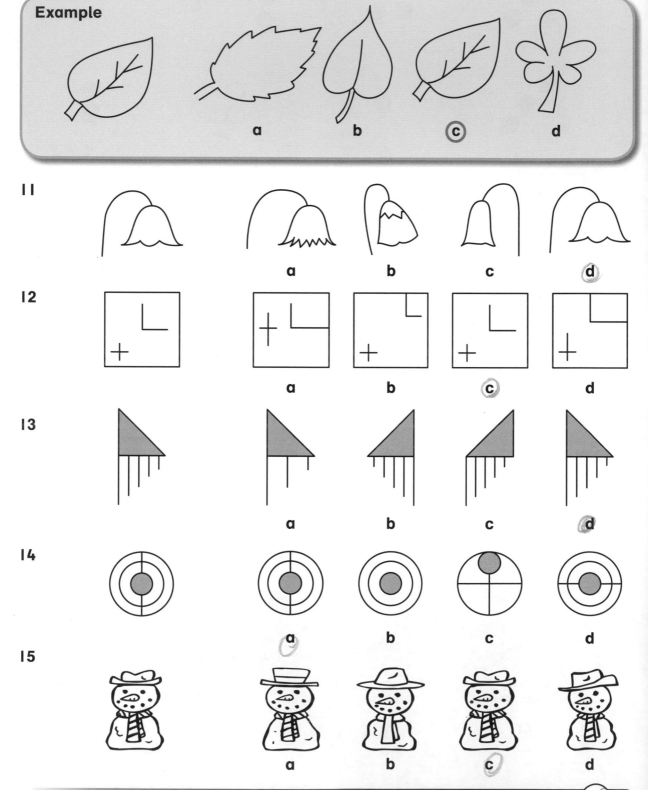

Example

a b ⓒ d

11

a b c ⓓ

12

a b ⓒ d

13

a b c ⓓ

14

ⓐ b c d

15

a b ⓒ d

Paper 8

Which one belongs to the group? Circle the letter.

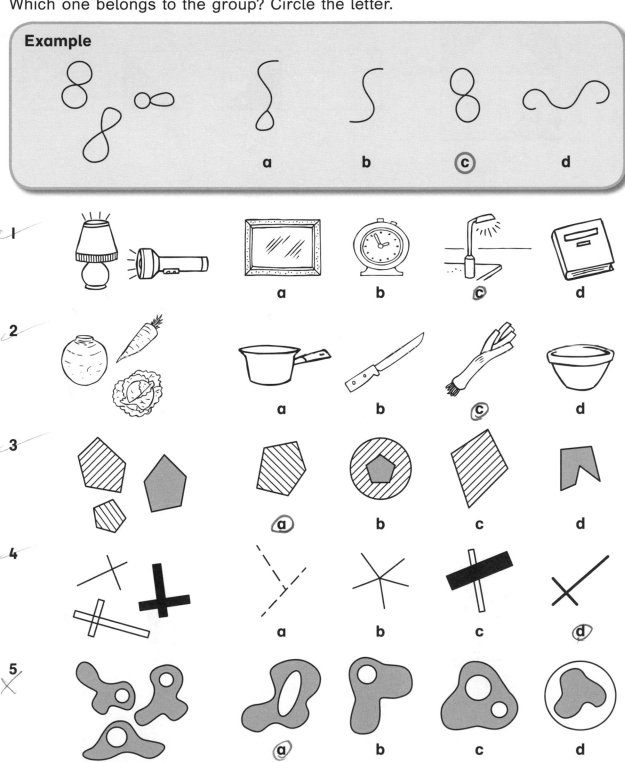

Example

1

2

3

4

5

Which one completes the pattern? Circle the letter.

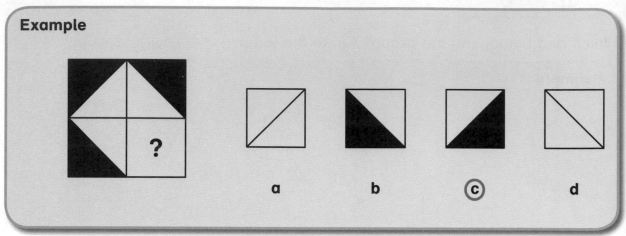

Example

a   b   ©   d

6

a   b   c   d

7

a   b   ©   d

8

      a   b   c   d

9

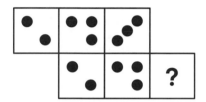

      a   b   c   d

10

      a   b   c   d

Which one completes the second pair in the same way as the first pair?
Circle the letter.

Example

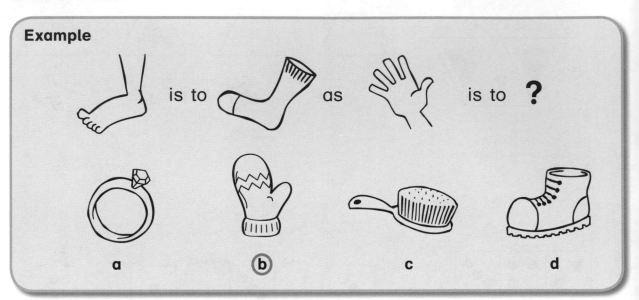

11

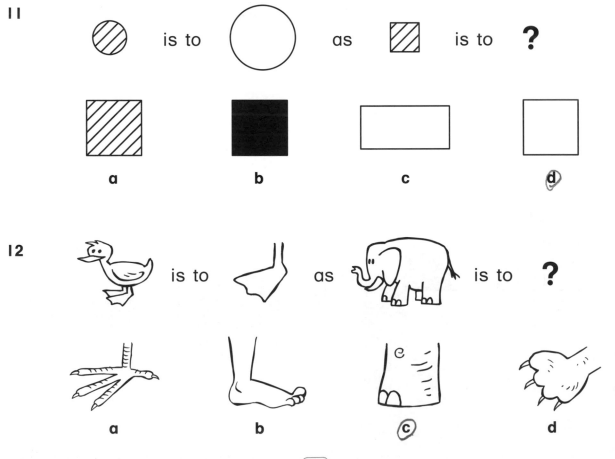

13

is to ⟨image⟩ as ⟨image⟩ is to **?**

a   b   c   d

14

is to ⟨image⟩ as ⟨image⟩ is to **?**

a   b   c   d

15

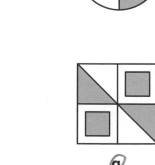

is to ⟨image⟩ as ⟨image⟩ is to **?**

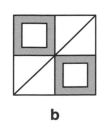   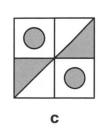   ⟨image⟩   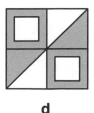

a   b   c   d

Progress Chart

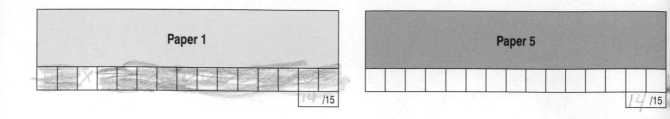

Paper 1 — 14 /15

Paper 5 — 14 /15

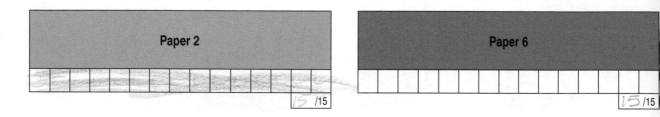

Paper 2 — 15 /15

Paper 6 — 15 /15

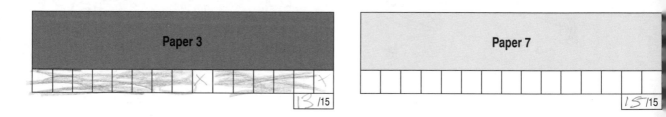

Paper 3 — 13 /15

Paper 7 — 15 /15

Paper 4 — 14 /15

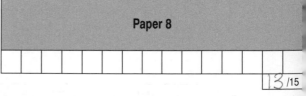

Paper 8 — 13 /15